To my beautiful Daughter

With love from

Other books in this series:

Best Friends
Thank you Mum
Have a Perfect Day
My Dad, My Hero
I've got a crush on you
Stay Calm
Happy Birthday
My Sister
Your Beautiful Baby

Published in 2013 by Helen Exley® Gifts in Great Britain. A copy of the CIP data is available from the British Library on request. All rights reserved. No part of this publication may be reproduced or transmitted in any form or by any means, electronic or mechanical, including photocopy, recording or any information storage and retrieval system without permission in writing from the Publisher. Printed in China.

Words and illustrations © Jenny Kempe 2013
Design and arrangement © Helen Exley Creative 2015
The moral right of the author has been asserted.

12 11 10 9 8 7 6

ISBN: 978-1-84634-607-1

Published by HELEN EXLEY®
Helen Exley Gifts, 16 Chalk Hill, Watford, Herts WD19 4BG, UK.
www.helenexley.com

Beautiful Daughter

WORDS AND ILLUSTRATIONS BY
JENNY KEMPE

I loved you
from the first moment
I saw you.

I loved seeing you

I discovered beauty again –
through your eyes.

You found
adventures and skills
and happiness...

I watched you growing up.

There were places to go
and friends to see;
Shoes to find and
shoes to buy. A world to see
and a world to save...

So many memories.
Doing so much,
just being friends
– always together.

But now you've become your own person.

You are my constant pride.

...and my constant worry.

You are grace.
You are beauty.

My world lights up with
your laughter.

The best birthday gift

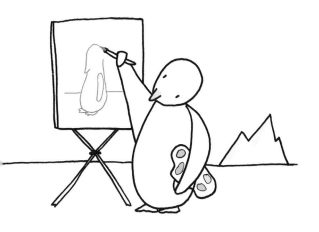

are those from you.

Of course, I live
your every crisis.

And your pain
is my pain.

I wish you joy.

Your happiness means more
than anything to me.

beginnings.

And to see you go?
Well, it does break my heart...

Deep down
I know:
...you will find your way.

My Beautiful Daughter

You have always been
my joy, my pride,
my most precious treasure.

I have always loved you.

And I always will.

Jenny Kempe

In 2009, overwhelmed by the endless bad news in the media, Jenny Kempe decided to take a six month break from newspapers, TV and radio. She turned her focus to the things in life that made her happy; to friends and family and to "taking time to just be". The result is the wonderfully bright and positive gift book series "Life is Beautiful". Each title has been designed to warm your heart and to put a smile on your face. As gifts, these books will brighten up the day, or even the life, of someone you care for.

www.jennykempe.com

We loved making this book for you.
We hope you'll enjoy the other titles
in our series Life is Beautiful.

The Life is Beautiful Team

About Helen Exley gifts

Our products cover the most powerful range of all human
relationships: love between couples, the bonds within families
and between friends. No expense is spared in making sure
that each book is as thoughtful and meaningful a gift as it is
possible to create: good to give, good to receive.
You have the result in your hands. If you have loved it –
tell others!

**Visit our website to see all of Helen Exley's other books
and gifts: www.helenexley.com**

Helen Exley Gifts
16 Chalk Hill, Watford, Herts
WD19 4BG, UK
www.helenexley.com